THIS ANNUAL BELONGS TO ME, SO...

You are now the proud owner of the latest, greatest **THUNDERCATS ANNUAL!** Make sure you personalise your copy by writing your name in the space below. That way, everyone'll know that it's your own personal property.

THIS BOOK BELONGS TO

Niceslas Timmarrman

23 Becowe gardens W.12

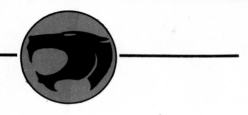

THUNDERCATS™ ANNUAL published by **MARVEL COMICS LTD.**, a New World Pictures Company, 23 Redan Place, London W2 4SA. Copyright ©1986 Leisure Concepts Inc., Telepictures Corporation and Ted Wolf. All rights reserved. Printed in Italy. No similarity between any of the names, characters, persons and/or institutions in this book with those of any living or dead person or institution is intended, and any such similarity is purely coincidental. THUNDERCATS and THUNDERCATS characters are Trademarks of Telepictures Corporation.

THUNDERCATS ANNUAL

CONTENTS

Welcome to the second superb **THUNDERCATS ANNUAL!** This year we've gone to even greater lengths to cram even more Thundercats action and adventure into this 64-page volume. Not only have we two full-length comic strip adventures — *Siege In Silver And Stone!* (from **Thundercats** 1&2), and *Jaga Quest* from **Thundercats** 3&4) — but we also have an all-new text story entitled *Way Back... When?*, which features more than the odd few shocks and surprises! In addition to all this Thundercats story excitement we've some superb Thundercats posters for your wall. It all adds up to a superb collection of the very best from the world of the Thundercats! And don't forget, the Thundercats action continues every week in pages of Marvel's **THUNDERCATS** comic.

DAVID MICHELINIE
WRITER
•
JIM MOONEY
PENCILS
•
BREEDING, MORGAN & CO.
INKS
•
JANICE CHIANG
LETTERS
•
NELSON YOMTOV
COLOURS
•
MIKE CARLIN
EDITOR
•
TOM DeFALCO
EXECUTIVE EDITOR
•
JIM SHOOT
EDITOR IN

BASED ON THE **THUNDERCATS** T.V. SERIES, A RANKIN/BASS PRODUCTION.

ThunderCats

AT A SHALLOW EXCAVATION SOME-WHERE IN THE WILDS OF THE PLANET CALLED THIRD EARTH, UNNATURAL LIGHTNING CRACKS THE DAWN--

--FORMING A SHINING BEACON THAT LEADS NOT FROM CLOUD GROUND, BUT FROM MAN-MADE METAL TO THE VERY SKY ITSE

IT IS BRILLIANCE BORN OF MAJESTY, AND FUELED BY THE PRIMAL POWER OF THUNDER. THUNDER... *THUNDER*...

THUNDERCATS-

--HO!

SIEGE I SILVER AND STON

6

LOOK! IT'S LION-O'S SIGNAL!

HE'S IN TROUBLE!

LET'S GO.

HOWEVER...

--WE'RE--

--HERE--

--LION-O!

WHERE'S THE DANGER?

WELL, UH, AS A MATTER OF FACT...

...THERE ISN'T ANY!

I JUST FINISHED USING THE LASER-TORCH TO CUT THERMOSTONE SHINGLES FOR INSULATION AT THE LAIR AND, WELL--

--I SORT OF THOUGHT I COULD GET THEM BACK A LOT QUICKER IF YOU GUYS HELPED ME.

WHAT?!

I DON'T BE-LIEVE THIS!

YOU'RE STILL LEARNING THE RESPONSIBILITIES OF BEING HEREDITARY LEADER OF THE THUNDERCATS, LION-O--

--BUT YOU MUST REALIZE THAT THE SWORD OF OMENS, AND THE EYE OF THUNDERA EMBEDDED IN ITS HILT, MUST NEVER, NEVER BE USED FRIVOLOUSLY.

YOU'RE RIGHT, TYGRA. I'M SORRY. I GUESS I WASN'T THINKING.

DON'T WORRY, LION-O, OL' SNARF'LL HELP YA OUT! AND COME TO THINK OF IT--

--WILYKIT AND WILYKAT DON'T HAVE ANY CHORES THIS AFTERNOON, EITHER! I'M SURE THE FOUR OF US CAN--

SORRY, SNARF, WE'RE GOING TO TEST DRIVE THE NEW *SPACEBOARDS* PANTHRO MADE FOR US!

YEAH, SEE YA!

"SPACEBOARDS"?! HMPH!

IN MY DAY, KIDS WEREN'T SO DOGGONED LAZY. -SNARF SNARF-

WHILE BACK AT CATS' LAIR...

GOING OUT ON ANOTHER SURVEY TRIP, PANTHRO?

NOT THIS TIME, CHEETARA. I NOTICED WE'RE RUNNING LOW ON *THUNDRILLIUM*, THE ELEMENT THAT PROVIDES POWER FOR THE LAIR--

-- SO I THOUGHT I'D HEAD OVER TO THE SOURCE QUARRY AND STOCK US A FRESH SUPPLY!

HMM, THE 'TANK IS RUNNING LOW ON FUEL, TOO. AH, WELL--

-- NO REASON TO TAP THE LAIR'S RESOURCES. I CAN ALWAYS REFUEL THE 'TANK AT THE QUARRY, TOO.

Time passes, as miles roll by easily beneath the hungry treads of the Thundertank.

Through the forest of enchanted unicorns, across the bridge of light, around the forest of giant insects and over the sifting, sibilant mass called sponge fog.

While ever sure-handed at the 'tank's helm...

Y'KNOW, I'M STARTING TO LIKE THIS WORLD. WHEN OUR HOME PLANET, *THUNDERA*, SLIPPED FROM ITS ORBIT, THE THUNDERCATS COULD'VE ENDED UP IN A LOT WORSE PLACES.

I MEAN, THINGS AREN'T EXACTLY EASY HERE, BUT AT LEAST THEY'RE NEVER--

EEEEEEE

--DULL?

L-LEAVE ME ALONE! G-G-GO AWAY!

YOUR PRESENCE HAS DEFILED THE HALLOWED REALM OF THE ROCKMEN, HUMAN!

AND FOR THAT YOU MUST APPEASE OUR GODS--AS A SACRIFICE!

PLEASE! I-I DON'T WANT TO... D-DON'T MAKE ME--!

True concern edges cold fear in the young woman's voice, as she pulls slowly at delicate silver rings on the fingers of each hand... an oddly reluctant action that is suddenly--

BUT SUCH A WONDERFUL MACHINE MUST SURELY HAVE WEAPONS! WHY NOT USE THEM?

WELL, MAINLY BECAUSE OF--

--NUTS. BECAUSE OF THAT!

WE'RE LOW ON POWER-- AND IT LOOKS LIKE THAT PEEL-OUT ESCAPE LEFT US EVEN LOWER!

BEEP BEEP BEEP

WE'LL NEVER BE ABLE TO OUTDISTANCE THOSE GOONS BEFORE--WAIT!

THAT CAVE!

MAYBE WE CAN HOLE UP IN THERE!

BUT THE ROCKMEN WILL SEE!

THEY'LL FOLLOW--!

NOT IF I USE THE LAST BIT OF THUNDRILLIUM--

--TO DO--

SHHHK SHHHK

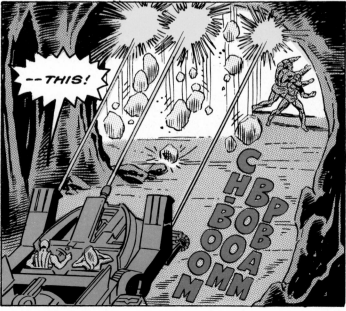

--THIS!

CHBPBOOOMM

11

RIGHT! THAT *SEAL* SHOULD KEEP THOSE *PEBBLE-PEOPLE* BUSY FOR A WHILE!

AND THE *FISSURES* IN THE CAVE ROOF SHOULD GIVE US ENOUGH LIGHT AND AIR TO STAY ALIVE!

THEN, WE'RE *SAFE?*

YEAH. SAFE.

FOR NOW...

WHILE AT CATS' LAIR...

WHEW! ME AN' MY BIG *VOLUNTEERIN'* MOUTH! THIS SHINGLE-LUGGIN' IS TOUGH WORK!

I'M *BUSHED!*

KLANKA LANK

AH, WELL, YAWWWUM! GUESS A LITTLE *NAP* BEFORE GOIN' BACK FOR ANOTHER LOAD WOULDN'T HURT ANYTHI––

12

--EEEEEYIPE!

NOT LYING DOWN ON THE JOB, ARE YOU, SNARF?

STILL LOTS OF WORK TO BE DONE!

WHA--? P-P-PUT ME DOWN, YOU... YOU AIR PIRATES.

IN MY DAY, ADULTS WEREN'T SO DOGGONED LAZY!

HA HA HA HA HA!

--OONF--

'HRRUMP!' THEY'RE JUST PICKIN' ON ME 'CAUSE I'M THE ONLY THUNDERCAT SMALLER'N THEM!

I'LL BET THIS WOULDN'T HAPPEN IF I WAS AS BIG AS PANTHRO!

I'M PANTHRO--

13

--AND YOU LOOK LIKE ONE OF THE WARRIOR MAIDENS WHO LIVE IN THE FOREST NEXT TO THE BOTTOMLESS CHASM.

I...WAS. I AM *TESSA*, AND I AM SORRY TO PUT YOU IN SUCH DANGER.

AH, THAT'S NO PROBLEM. I'M KINDA USED TO IT.

I JUST WISH WE HAD MORE OF A FIGHTIN' CHANCE. I'D GIVE *ANYTHING* FOR A WEAPON TO USE AGAINST--

NO! DON'T SAY THAT!

DON'T *EVER* SAY THAT!

WHAT THE--?

I...I-I'M SORRY, IT'S JUST THAT PEOPLE DON'T UNDERSTAND...TH-THEY DON'T REALIZE THERE MAY BE A *PRICE* FOR...WELL, PERHAPS I SHOULD EXPLAIN.

I WISH YOU *WOULD!*

YOU SEE...

"...IT WASN'T SO LONG AGO THAT I *DID* LIVE IN THE TREETOP VILLAGE OF THE WARRIOR MAIDENS.

"I AND MY SISTERS WORKED HARD, PROSPERED, AND WERE HAPPY.

14

"BUT THAT CONTENTMENT WAS NOT TO LAST. THROUGH CIRCUMSTANCES THAT NEED NOT BE REPEATED HERE, OUR TRIBE INCURRED THE WRATH OF THE WIZARD CALLED *MUMM-RA*, AND AGAINST US HE SENT THE DREADFUL THING KNOWN AS--

"--DAGGER MIST!"

"WE HAD NO DEFENCE, NO WAY TO FIGHT THE CREATURE.

"FEAR AND DESPAIR SPREAD LIKE WILDFIRE AS WE FACED NOT ONLY DEATH, BUT THE POTENTIAL EXTINCTION OF OUR ENTIRE RACE!

"THE MIST'S TENDRILS WERE ABLE TO CUT THROUGH WOOD AND STONE ALIKE, DEVASTATING OUR VILLAGE--

"-- WHILE OUR WEAPONS STRUCK IT WITH NO MORE DAMAGE THAN BREEZES PASSING THROUGH MORNING FOG!

"IT WAS THEN THAT I SWORE I WOULD NOT LET SUCH A THING HAPPEN. I WOULD FIND A WEAPON TO USE AGAINST THE DAGGER MIST--AND I WOULD DO *ANYTHING* TO GAIN IT!

"THUS I SOUGHT ANCIENT KNOWLEDGE, ARCANE SORCERIES THAT HAD BEEN FORBIDDEN FOR AGES.

"WE HAD ALL BEEN WARNED, FROM CRIB-TIME ONWARD, OF THE DANGERS OF USING SUCH FORCES. BUT I IGNORED THE WARNINGS.

"I FOUND WAYS TO WEAVE A SPELL, ONE THAT FILLED ME WITH DARKLING POWER!

"UNNAMED ENERGIES FLOWED THROUGH MY BEING AS IF I HAD BECOME A LIVING BATTERY!

"AND SO, ARMED WITH THOSE ENERGIES—AS WELL AS MORE COURAGE THAN I HAD EVER BELIEVED I POSSESSED— I CONFRONTED THE DAGGER MIST—

"AND I WON.

"JOY WAS EVERYWHERE. THE VILLAGE WAS SAVED! I RAISED MY HANDS IN TRIUMPH!

"AND VERY NEARLY KILLED WILLA, OUR TRIBAL LEADER, WITH AN ACCIDENTAL ENERGY BURST!

"FOR THOUGH I HAD INDEED GAINED GREAT POWER, I HAD NO TRUE MASTERY OVER IT!

LUCKILY, WE SOON FOUND THAT SILVER COULD IMPEDE THE ERRANT ENERGY BLASTS, AND SO RINGS OF THAT METAL WERE AFFIXED TO EACH OF MY FINGERS. THE DANGER ABATED--

"--BUT STILL, THE UNSPOKEN FEAR REMAINED: WHAT IF THE SILVER SHOULD BECOME INEFFECTIVE? IF A RING SHOULD FALL OFF WHILE I SLEPT?

"I NOW POSSESSED A POTENTIAL FOR DEATH AND DESTRUCTION THAT WAS AT LEAST EQUAL TO THE DAGGER MIST--AND I KNEW IT AS WELL AS EVERYONE.

"SO I DID WHAT HAD TO BE DONE. I LEFT THE VILLAGE, MY FRIENDS... MY SISTERS.

OR THE GOOD OF US ALL.

"AND THAT DECISION HAS PROVEN A WISE ONE. OVER THE DAYS, THE POWER I CARRY HAS BECOME EVEN MORE ERRATIC. I KNOW NOT HOW MUCH LONGER THE RINGS CAN KEEP IT IN CHECK.

"I WAS EVEN AFRAID TO UNLEASH IT AGAINST THOSE ROCKMEN, LEST I LOSE CONTROL OVER IT COMPLETELY! IF YOU HADN'T INTERVENED...

BUT FOR HOW LONG?

YEAH, WELL, I DID. AND WE'RE SAFE NOW.

THE ROCKMEN ARE STARTING TO *BREAK THROUGH* THE SEAL!

UH, I WAS KINDA HOPING YOU WOULDN'T NOTICE THAT...

WHILE LEAGUES DISTANT, AT THE THERMOSTONE QUARRY...

SNARF JUST LEFT WITH HIS LAST LOAD, AND AS SOON AS I GET THIS ONE BACK TO THE LAIR--

HMMMMMMM

--EH? THE EYE OF THUNDERA! WARNING OF *DANGER!*

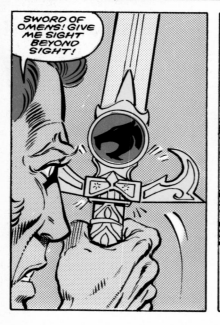

SWORD OF OMENS! GIVE ME SIGHT *BEYOND* SIGHT!

PANTHRO! AND ONE OF THE WARRIOR MAIDENS! *TRAPPED* IN A CAVE -- AND BEING *ATTACKED* BY ROCKMEN!

I'VE GOT TO SUMMON THE OTHER THUNDERCATS AND--

--NO! I USED THE SUMMONING TOO QUICKLY BEFORE, AND ALL IT GOT ME WAS A TONGUE-LASHING! THIS TIME--

--I'LL HANDLE THINGS ON MY OWN!

HOWEVER, IN HIS ZEAL TO AID HIS FRIEND--

--LION-O FAILS TO NOTICE THE STRANGELY-SLITHERING VINES THAT SPRAWL IN SEEMING RANDOM ACROSS THE SHADOWED JUNGLE PATH.

--UNTIL...

TWANGG

TANG

PTWANG

WHUP--?!

THESE VINES! TH-THEY'RE ALIVE! T-TRYING TO PULL ME APART!

AND THE SWORD! O-OUT OF REACH!

WHAT'LL I DO NOW?

WHAT WILL WE DO NOW, PANTHRO? THE ROCKMEN ARE ALMOST THROUGH THE SEAL!

"ALMOST" IS BETTER THAN "ALREADY", TESSA! BESIDES--

-- YOUR STORY GAVE ME AN IDEA! THAT'S WHY I'VE BEEN TINKERIN' WITH THE THUNDERTANK'S ENGINE! SEE THESE GADGETS?

I'VE JERRY-RIGGED PART OF THE 'TANK'S FUEL MECHANISM TO ACT AS A POWER CONVERTOR. IF MY THEORY WORKS--

-- IT SHOULD BE ABLE T' DRAIN YOUR ENERGY, T' USE IT AS A SUBSTITUTE FOR THUNDRILLIUM WHILE AT THE SAME TIME FREEIN' YOU FROM THE DANGER O' SHOOTING ACCIDENTAL BLASTS!

ALL YOU HAVE TO DO IS PUT YOUR HANDS IN THE RECEPTACLES--THE MACHINE WILL DO THE REST. JUST TAKE OFF THOSE RINGS AND--

NO!

I-IT'S TOO DANGEROUS! I CAN'T CONTROL THE POWER! EVEN IF I WERE ABLE TO TRANSFER IT TO THE VEHICLE, THE DEVICE MIGHT OVERLOAD! IT MIGHT BLOW UP!

PANTHRO, IT MIGHT KILL YOU!

THE WAY I SEE IT, TESSA, WE'RE BETWEEN A ROCKMAN AND A HARD PLACE.

WE DON'T HAVE MUCH CHOICE.

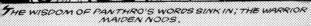

THE WISDOM OF PANTHRO'S WORDS SINK IN; THE WARRIOR MAIDEN NODS.

AND ONE BY ONE, WITH AS MUCH TREPIDATION AS DETERMINATION, SHE SLOWLY SLIPS THE SLENDER SILVER CIRCLES FROM HER FINGERS.

PANTHRO! TH-THE POWER! I--IT'S STARTING TO FLOW!

I CAN'T STOP IT!

QUICK, TESSA! PUT YOUR HANDS IN!

NOW!

NOW!

ENERGY SURGES AND CRACKLES! FOUL LIGHTNING LEAPS IN THE RECEPTACLES! AND TESSA SCREAMS...

WHILE OUTSIDE...

SOON, MY STONEMATES! ANOTHER CRUSHING BLOW, AND THE DEFILERS WILL BE OURS!

ONE... TWO...

KRAKAAAASSH

SHAKAM

PRAKOW

BADOWN

OKAY, CREEPS, LET'S SEE WHAT YOU CAN DO AGAINST THUNDERTANK ON *FULL POWER!*

AAAAAYEEAAAAA!

WHAT'S THE MATTER? PARTY NOT SO MUCH FUN WHEN SOMEONE *ELSE* BRINGS THE FAVOURS?

WE DID IT! THEY'RE FLEEING!

YEAH, JUST LOOK AT THOSE COBBLEHEADS RUN!

AND IT WAS YOUR POWER THAT DID IT, TESSA!

NO, IT IS MY POWER NO LONGER. BECAUSE OF YOU, ANTHRO, AT LAST--

-- I AM FREE!

GOTTA GET... FREE! BUT THESE VINES ARE TOO STRONG! C-CAN'T BREAK THEM! C-CAN'T EVEN REACH THE TREES THEY'RE GROWING FROM--

-- WAIT! THAT'S IT! THE TREES! TREES HAVE--

-- ROOTS!

CHRUNCH

KRRRRIP

DID IT! WITH THE ROOTS RIPPED UP, THE VINES ARE GOING LIMP, LETTING GO! BUT WHAT ABOUT--

23

--PANTHRO

SWORD OF OMENS GIVE ME SIGHT BEYOND SIGHT!

HE'S SAFE! THEY'RE BOTH SAFE! THAT'S TERRIFIC! THEY DID GREAT! JUST GREAT...

...WITHOUT ME.

AND SOON, AMIDST THE BRANCHED BYWAYS OF THE WARRIOR MAIDENS' WONDROUS TREETOP VILLAGE...

YOU HAVE RETURNED TO US AFTER AN ABSENCE BOTH OVERLONG AND PAINFUL. WELCOME, TESSA...

24

...WELCOME HOME.

THANK YOU, WILLA.

I ALWAYS DID LIKE HAPPY ENDINGS!

I OWE YOU EVERYTHING, PANTHRO. BUT ALL I HAVE TO GIVE IS--

--THIS, TO REMEMBER ME BY.

AND THIS, AS A TOKEN OF MY GRATITUDE UNDYING.

THAT MAY BE ALL YOU HAVE, TESSA, BUT FOR ME... IT'S PLENTY!

FROM THE GATHERED CROWD, A ROUSING CHEER RISES.

25

THIS LOAD OF THUNDRILLIUM SHOULD LAST US FOR MONTHS, PANTHRO. DID YOU HAVE ANY TROUBLE GETTING IT HERE?

CHEETARA, YOU WOULDN'T BELIEVE ME IF I TOLD YOU!

NO, BUT *I* WOULD. I SHOULD HAVE *BEEN* THERE, AND IF I'D CALLED IN THE OTHER THUNDERCATS I WOULD HAVE! THEY COULD HAVE CUT ME LOOSE FROM THOSE VINES!

WE ALL COULD HAVE HELPED PANTHRO!

HINDSIGHT CAN BE A USEFUL TOOL, LION-O--

--BUT ONLY IF YOU USE IT TO GAIN *FORESIGHT*.

WHA-- JAGA! Y-YOU WERE WATCHING IN YOUR SPIRIT FORM?

I WAS.

THEN YOU SAW ME MAKE A FOOL OF MYSELF.

NO, LION-O. HOPEFULLY, I SAW YOU *LEARN*. I SAW YOU DISCOVER THAT CALLING ON FRIENDS FOR SELFISH MOTIVES IS WRONG-- BUT THAT *NOT* CALLING WHEN YOU TRULY NEED THEM IS WORSE.

AND NOW THAT YOU'VE SEEN THE ERROR, I'M CERTAIN THAT YOU WON'T REPEAT IT.

YOU'RE RIGHT, JAGA. I WON'T. AND THANKS-- I KNOW I CAN ALWAYS COUNT ON YOU TO MAKE ME FEEL BETTER.

OLD FRIEND, I DON'T KNOW WHAT I'D EVER DO WITHOUT--

CONTINUED ON PAGE 34

WAY BACK... WHEN?
PART ONE

Plot **SIMON FURMAN** ● Story **STEVE ALAN** ● Illustrations **RADBOURNE** and **BASKERVILLE** ● Colour **STEVE WHITE**

On the third day of the march, Lion-O dreamt of rain. It was easy to sleep, listening to the soft, rhythmic pat of feet on the parched desert sand, hearing the faint rattle of their chains. Trouble was, as they marched not only by day, but also by night — it was only possible to sleep on the move. And so, racked with thirst, on the verge of exhaustion, Lion-O marched, and dozed, and gradually overcame his natural feline aversion to water.

It was just as he encountered an especially refreshing dream-cloudburst that Lion-O was jarred rudely awake. His lip curled in a faint snarl. Who dared disturb the slumber of the Lord of the Thundercats?

29

He raised a weary head, scanning the line of assorted humanoid and alien creatures who were his fellow prisoners. It was the hulking, silent anthropoid, manacled just in front of Lion-O, who had stumbled and fallen. Lion-O had spoken to the creature only once, when the Thugron Slavers had manacled them together. 'Ho, friend — what brings you to this barren place?' The anthropoid's curt 'Button your lip, catface, or I'll tie it shut with your whiskers!' had tended to discourage further conversation. But now he was clearly in trouble, and one of the Thugron Slavers was already galloping back from the head of the procession, electro-lash whirling threateningly!

Lion-O felt a rough paw grasp his shoulder, and turned to meet the urgent glare of his fellow Thundercat, Panthro. 'No, Lion-O', Panthro warned. 'It's not our fight — you'll only get hurt'. Lion-O glanced behind him to where Tygra, Cheetara, Wily Kat and Wily Kit trudged, also in chains. Their faces were drawn, muzzles streaked with sand and dirt, but the message in all their eyes was the same. Lion-O blinked once and turned, to where the Thugron Slaver now reared, electro-lash still whirling like a lariat about his head. The fallen anthropoid still lay in the sand between them.

'Can't you let us rest for a while, sir?' said Lion-O, with a broad grin. 'This poor fellow is much too tired to walk any further'. He continued to smile as the Thugron leaned down from his mount, thrusting his bull-like face within centimetres of Lion-O's own. Folds of green fat rippled in barely controlled rage.

'That so?' purred the Thugron through gritted fangs, the stale waft of a best-forgotten meal crawling across Lion-O. 'Then maybe you'd like to take his share of the Tasp, fur-ball!' As he uncoiled the electro-lash, Lion-O grabbed it, yanking the Slaver clear of his horse. Needles of acid pain swarmed up his arm as Lion-O gripped the Tasp, winding it tight about the struggling guard's neck. The Thugron's flabby legs flailed uselessly above the sand as he thrashed and gurgled, in pain, and outrage, and finally fear. Letting go, Lion-O knocked him unconscious with a flying kick and overbalanced in the sand, panting. 'Don't call me fur-ball, bucket-face!'

'Nice goin', Lion-O', Panthro smiled wearily. 'But what about his friends?' Two more Thugron Slavers had now reached the scene, and the deadly tongues of their Tasps reached Lion-O almost simultaneously. The double shock sent him hurtling backwards, to land in a pained heap on the sand. The other Thundercats surged forward, only to stop short as the remaining Thugrons trained ugly vibro-cannons on them. 'Anyone else here want to rest?' said the first Thugron sulkily, remounting his horse and galloping to the head of the procession.

'Thanks, catface', gruffed the fallen anthropoid, now fully conscious, as they resumed the march. 'Guess I wasn't over-friendly just before'.

'Seems to be catching', said Lion-O stiffly, massaging life back into his tingling muscles. 'And *don't* call me catface — my name is Lion-O'.

'Sorry', the anthropoid grinned sheepishly. 'I'm Zar-Thule — but you can call me Zar. Who are you people, anyway? How did you get here?'.

Lion-O sighed. The effect of the Tasps was wearing off, but in its wake was a dreadful, bone-weary fatigue. 'It's a long story', he said. Zar-Thule snorted. 'We seem to have plenty of time'.

And so Lion-O told of the lush green world of *Thundera*, homeworld of the Thundercats. Of the feather meadows, the singing rains — and of the terrible day that their beloved planet began swinging slowly and relentlessly out of orbit, toward the sun.

A fleet of starships had escaped the dying corona of Thundera as gravitational forces finally tore it apart. Lion-O told of their harsh and often perilous quest for a new home, and of their eventual planetfall on Third Earth. He spoke of the Cat's Lair, the Plain of Fertility — eagerly wishing he was back there.

'I don't get it, catface', interrupted Zar-Thule as Lion-O's story tailed off into rambling homesickness. 'Cat's Lair? Plain of Fertility? I know every inch of this world, and I've never heard of those places. Or of the Thundercats, for that matter'.

'Then you've been poorly informed, friend', interjected Panthro, bristling with the pride of a Noble. 'The fame of the Thundercats is hailed from the Bridge Of Light to the Kingdom of the Snowmen in the south'.

'Not in my neck of the jungle, grey stuff', snapped Zar-Thule. 'Where in the Blue Vase of Ghosts is this 'Bridge of Light', anyway? And if you Thundercats are so sensational, how did you manage to get yourselves captured by those pug-uglies up ahead?'. Lion-O frowned. the circumstances of their capture *had* been peculiar. It had begun in the Swamp Of Serpents, during a routine exploration in the Thundertank.

There was, of course, no such thing as a routine exploration of Third Earth. In their few short months on the little planet, each of the Thundercats had learned to keep a wary eye out for the local plant and animal life, an awful lot of which was unnervingly hostile. As it was that day in the Swamp Of Serpents, when Lion-O and Panthro encountered the Astral Moat Monster.

The Astral Moat Monster was in a particularly bad mood. This was partly because there was no Astral Moat to guard anymore, which left him at

rather a loss for something to do. But the root cause of the Astral Moat Monster's ill humour could be traced back much further — thousands of years in fact — to when he was grown in the Chemical Pits of Grizquetr. An incompetent spellbinder had left him in the life-giving fluids just a fraction too long, bloating his ducklike blue body out of proportion, gifting him with a pair of ridiculous (and quite useless) red wings, and speckling his huge slack mouth with teeth like ill-fitting dagger rocks.

The Astral Moat Monster's pride and joy had been the Astral Moat, which he guarded fiercely. So fiercely, in fact, that if fell into total disuse, soaking into the earth to be overgrown by a limp grey pondweed. The Moat Monster continued to march up and down looking peevish and dangerous for a few years after that, but a lot of the fun had gone out of it.

One day, in a boiling, suicidal rage, he had dived headlong into the murky waters of the Swamp Of Serpents, and there he had slept, angrily, for hundreds of years. And now, as the gutteral roar of the Thundertank disturbed his agelong sulk, the Astral Moat Monster bunched his ghastly claws into fists. It was time to get *really* angry.

'We're sinking, Panthro', Lion-O said warningly, as the Thundertank floundered in the primeval murk of the swamp. 'Not to worry, Young Lord', came Panthro's voice from the twin cockpit. 'That's what the flotation chambers are for'. Lion-O watched tensely through the windscreen as the Thundertank began to right itself, and it was then that something caught his eye.

Possibly the most ridiculous creature Lion-O had ever seen was slowly rising from the swamp, directly in front of the Thundertank. It was huge and blue, that much was certain. As it swayed its grinning, unsightly way toward them, a tiny pair of useless red wings fluttered foolishly about its shoulders. 'Panthro!' Lion-O gasped, trying to stifle a laugh. He needn't have bothered — Panthro's rich guffaws were already booming across from the other cockpit.

'It's the wings, isn't it?' bawled the Astral Moat Monster sorrowfully. 'Don't bother denying it!' Aiming a monstrous kick at the Thundertank, he howled in pain and fury as he discovered that those hundreds of years in the Swamp Of Serpents had given him a dreadful case of bunions. Abruptly, Lion-O and Panthro stopped laughing as each was buffeted cruelly against the vibranium walls of the Thundertank. Dazed, Panthro thumbed the cockpit toggle, staggering clear of the vehicle into soft, marshy earth.

Numbchucks whirling, he launched into action, but recovery had come just a fraction too late. Without even seeming to notice, the Astral Moat Monster snapped his fingers closed around the numbchucks, wrenching them from Panthro's helpless grip. 'My foot!' wailed the Monster, as though expecting some display of sympathy. 'My foooot!' he repeated, swatting Panthro unconscious with a spadelike hand.

The Astral Moat Monster forgot all about his foot a moment later, as a powerful thunderclap rent the air. The other cat-creature had also escaped its machine, now listing badly in the soupy earth, and was pointing a sword skywards.

'Thunder. . .Thunder. . .Thunder. . .Thundercats — Ho!' Though young, the creature's voice rang with a commanding confidence beyond its years. The Astral Moat Monster shifted his blood shot gaze to the scarlet pillar of light that cut through the sky, painting the image of a cat's head on the black clouds. 'Might've known it would rain', he sniffed wretchedly. However, the thunder quickly subsided, replaced by a rustling in the surrounding undergrowth.

A female cat-creature, whom the leader called Cheetara, was the first to appear, bounding sinuously into the clearing to land in a soundless crouch. Next came a heavier male, Tygra, harsh tongues of flame striping his body as he leapt into the fray, nostrils aflare. A clattering of branches above the Monster was followed by the graceless plunge of Wilykat and Wilykit, two kitten creatures, crashing to the mossy earth in gales of chittering laughter. Lastly a scratty, yellow bearded animal swung into view, narrowly missing the nearby branches with its ribbed tail and landing with a soft PLOOK at the Astral Moat Monster's throbbing red feet. 'Dunno what this thing is, your cubship', said the bearded creature, 'But I bet it doesn't know any jokes, snarf snarf.'

'Speak, unpleasant one!' demanded Lion-O. 'Why did you attack the Thundertank?' The Astral Moat Monster surveyed the cat-creatures in mournful rage, realising that he hadn't the faintest idea what to say next. Instead he ground his teeth and blew some steam from his huge nostrils. Wilykat and Wilykit giggled louder. 'You're all going to die a most grisly death!' he bellowed. There was an embarrassing silence.

What happened next took everyone by surprise. With a sound like the tolling of some celestial bell, a great tear appeared in the milky paleness of the sky. All watched in fear and wonderment, as a howling gale began to brew, tiny flickers of crimson lightning dancing about the raw wound in the clouds. 'Doesn't anything ordinary ever happen on this planet? groaned Tygra, but no-one was listening. Lion-O was first, sucked carelessly into the updraught, tumbling skywards. Next were Wilykat and Wilykit, snatched aloft on the invisible fingers of the storm. As Tygra and Cheetara, and finally the unconscious Panthro followed, the Astral Moat Monster looked down at the small, yellow bearded cat-thing, now fastened securely to his ankle. 'I'm afraid of heights', offered Snarf lamely. 'Then prepare to be afraid of depths, puny one', cried the Astral Moat Monster, raising his arms to dive beneath the swamp. But before the sentence was over, he and Snarf were already some distance above the ground.

'We never did see Snarf again', concluded Lion-O sadly. 'When we woke we were here', he motioned to the desert around them, as Zar-Thule nodded earnestly. 'Half buried in sand, and feeling as though we'd been turned inside-out. I guess we were easy prey for the Thugrons'. He glanced ahead, glowering. One of the Thugrons was brandishing the stolen Sword Of Omens about his head, his coarse, tribal laughter drifting through the ranks.

'That's some story', said Zar-Thule wonderingly. 'Not saying I disbelieve you, mind — specially in view of where we're headed'.

'You know where we're going?' Lion-O's ears swivelled forward in intense curiosity. 'Oh sure — no big secret there. Word is we're to be slaves to the big cheese himself — Pharoah Ka-Rey-Bar'. 'Who?' All six Thundercats chorused in unison. A short, explosive laugh escaped Zar-Thule. 'Maybe you people are from another planet, at that', he snorted. 'See that place up ahead?' He indicated into the middle distance, where the canted walls of a polished onyx pyramid now loomed, glimmering in the noonday heat. 'That's the home of Ka-Rey-Bar', Zar-Thule continued. 'Only the pharoah of all known kingdoms, that's all'. None of the Thundercats spoke. Each was eyeing the onyx pyramid and its surrounding obelisks with mingled recognition and unease.

'Course', Zar-Thule was saying, 'Ka-Rey-Bar's not the one we need to worry about. It's his sorceror who's the real threat. They say he can summon spirits of ancient evil from the depths of Hell, or something similar. Personally, the Thugrons have got me about as worried as I ever want to be. Demons I don't need'.

Beyond the pyramid, on the banks of a lush river valley, lay a magnificent palace, its marble domes and jade towers climbing high into the cloudless sky. The prisoners were given no time to enjoy the view as the Thugrons herded them unceremoniously inside. In contrast to the pitiless heat of the long march, the antechamber of the palace of Ka-Rey-Bar was cool and dank. Shadows writhed across the poorly lit stone walls. As the Thugron Slavers approached to unshackle their captives, Lion-O exchanged a wordless signal with his fellow Thundercats.

The Thugrons were taken completely by surprise. In as dazzling a display of acrobatics as the weary Thundercats could muster, they fanned out, encircling their brutish captors. Wilykat, at the apex of the circle, launched himself from Panthro's great shoulders while Wilykit, directly opposite, catapulted herself upward from Tygra's. Together they darted, weaving in and around the startled Thugrons, snatching the coiled Tasps from their belts. Seconds later each of the Thundercats had a Tasp, which they cracked in the air above the Thugrons, knotting the ends in a lethally crackling display. Then they brought the completed web down.

The effect was instantaneous; the combined charge of the Tasps felled the screaming Slavers like a herd of rogue elephants. As the last of the Thugrons toppled like a great oak, Zar-Thule turned to Lion-O, eyes shining with respect and awe. 'What did you do?' was all he could gasp. Lion-O laughed for the first time in a number of days. 'Ever hear of a Cat's Cradle?' he grinned, as Cheetara tossed him the recovered Sword Of Omens.

'Predictable as ever, Lion-O', boomed a hauntingly familiar voice from the shadows. The other prisoners fell to the stone floor, faces stark with sudden terror. 'Unfortunately, you never really had a cat's chance'. Chilling laughter sounded, like the cawing of some monstrous bird of prey, and as a howling gale tore through the antechamber, all six Thundercats were cast into the air, and slammed brutally onto the cold flagstones. Lion-O could barely raise his head as he fought for breath. 'Show yourself!' he hissed. 'What game are you playing? Where on Third Earth *are* we?' Again crazed laughter reverberated from the dim walls. 'Whoever he is', gasped Wilykat, 'He's sure having a good time'.

A figure stepped out of the shadows. Lion-O almost didn't recognise the face, which was fuller; smoother. In a thousand years every evil path he had ever walked would be mapped out in its rotting folds, but for now, only the eyes were the same. Glowing, reddened orbs, curdled with insanity and the lust for power. Lion-O remembered at last where he had seen the onyx pyramid before.

'In answer to your question, cubling, you are nowhere on *Third* Earth at all! Another gale of wild cackling accompanied his words as the intruder raised his hands, tiny flickers of crimson lightning dancing about his fingers. 'The Dimensional Portal was a creation of mine, boy. It was *I* who plucked you — from my own future — through the winds of time to *First* Earth. To the first dynasty of Mumm-Ra, the Ever Living!' And he laughed again, and again, until it seemed the laughter would never stop.

'That's who I was telling you about', said Zar-Thule dolefully.

CONTINUED ON PAGE 57

33

THUNDERCATS

JAGA QUEST!

BASED ON THE **THUNDERCATS** T.V. SERIES, A RANKIN/BASS PRODUCTION.

LIFE ON THIRD EARTH HAS NOT BEEN EASY FOR THE THUNDERCATS. DAYS OF DANGER AND NIGHTS OF MENACE HAVE BEEN SOOTHED ONLY BY THE CLOSENESS OF THEIR NUMBER, BY THE COMRADESHIP BETWEEN THE SOLE KNOWN SURVIVORS OF THE EXTINCT PLANET, THUNDERA!

BUT NOW EVEN THAT COMFORT HAS BEEN TAKEN AWAY, SHATTERED BY THE SINISTER, UNEXPLAINED DISAPPEARANCE OF ONE OF THEIR OWN! AND NO THUNDERCAT ALIVE WILL REST—

—UNTIL THAT FRIEND IS FOUND!

DAVID MICHELINIE WRITER • **JIM MOONEY** PENCILS • **BRETT BREEDING** INKS • **JANICE CHIANG** LETTERS • **PETRA SCOTESE** COLOURS • **MIKE CARLIN** EDITOR • **TOM DeFALCO** EXECUTIVE EDITOR • **JIM SHOOTER** EDITOR IN CHIEF

HURRY WILYKIT! I WANT TO BE THE FIRST TO FIND A CLUE!

NO PROBLEM, WILYKAT! OUR SPACEBOARDS CAN BEAT THE THUNDERTANK ANY DAY!

'KAT AND 'KIT DON'T SEEM TO BE TAKING THIS VERY SERIOUSLY, PANTHRO.

DON'T SELL 'EM SHORT, TYGRA. THEY MAY TALK LIGHT, BUT THEY'RE THUNDERCATS-- THEY'LL GET THE JOB DONE.

COME ON, SNARF! WE'VE GOT A LOT OF GROUND TO COVER!

YEAH, THAT'S EASY TO SAY WHEN YOU'VE GOT THE SPEED OF A CHEETAH! ¡PUFF¡

WAIT UP!

THE THUNDERCATS ARE THE BEST FRIENDS ANYONE COULD HAVE. IF *JAGA* IS TO BE FOUND, THEY'LL FIND HIM, NO--

--WE'LL FIND HIM!

FEELING AS DETERMINED AS HE IS CONFIDENT, LION-O, LORD OF THE THUNDERCATS, SPRINTS INTO THE SURROUNDING JUNGLE--

--UNAWARE OF THE MYSTERIOUS FIGURE THAT PERCHES CAUTIOUSLY ON A TREE LIMB NEARBY, A FIGURE THAT WATCHES... AND SOFTLY PURRS.

WE'LL SEARCH EVERY INCH OF THIRD EARTH IF WE HAVE TO-- BUT WILL THAT BE *ENOUGH*?

WE DON'T EVEN KNOW IF JAGA IS STILL ON THIS *PLANET*!

"JAGA'S SPIRIT WAS TALKING TO ME, ADVISING ME AS HE HAS SO OFTEN DONE IN THE PAST, WHEN SUDDENLY--

"-- HE SCREAMED AND VANISHED LIKE SMOKE IN A HURRICANE!"*

*THIS HAPPENED LAST ISSUE!

"I TOLD TYGRA IMMEDIATELY, AND HE CALLED AN EMERGENCY COUNCIL MEETING..."

NONE BUT LION-O CAN SEE JAGA'S SPIRIT FORM. BUT LION-O IS OUR HEREDITARY LEADER--

--AND WE *MUST* BELIEVE THAT WHAT HE TELLS US IS TRUE.

THEREFORE, ALL OTHER PROJECTS ARE TO BE SET ASIDE. ALTHOUGH LION-O IS THE ONLY ONE WHO CAN ACTUALLY *FIND* JAGA, OUR TOP PRIORITY WILL BE TO SEEK OUT CLUES--

--SO THAT WE MAY HELP LION-O BRING JAGA *BACK* TO US!

BUT THAT MIGHT BE TOUGHER THAN WE THOUGHT. THIS WORLD IS A BIG PLACE, AND JAGA COULD BE ANYWHERE! ANYWHERE AT ALL--

LION-O!

WHA--JAGA! --BUT HOW--? WH-WH-WHERE--?

CALM YOURSELF, YOUNG LORD.

AN UNEXPECTED SURGE IN THE PSYCHIC FIELDS OF THIRD EARTH CAUSED ME TO FADE TEMPORARILY.

BUT THE EFFECT HAS PASSED, AND SHOULD NOT OCCUR AGAIN. I AM SORRY FOR ANY CONCERN I MAY HAVE CAUSED YOU.

I'M JUST GLAD YOU'RE BACK, JAGA! I DON'T KNOW WHAT I'D DO WITHOUT YOU!

BUT NOW I'D BETTER GO TELL THE OTHERS! THEY'LL BE AS RELIEVED AS I AM!

YES, WHY DON'T YOU DO THAT...

...FOOL!

AND SOON, AT THE MIGHTY FORTRESS CALLED **CATS' LAIR**...

PANTHRO? CHEETARA? WILYKAT? THIS IS LION-O!

I'VE FOUND JAGA! AND HE'S JUST FINE. LOOKS LIKE ALL OF OUR WORRIES WERE FOR NOTHING

I GUESS YOU GUYS CAN HEAD BACK TO THE LAIR NOW.

ON OUR WAY, LION-O!

RACE YOU BACK, WILYKAT!

MESSAGE ACKNOWLEDGED. THAT'S GOOD NEWS, LION-O.

IT IS INDEED.

WELL, IF NOTHING ELSE WE GOT SOME EXERCISE.

LET'S GO HOME, SNARF!

NOW?! B-BUT, COULDN'T WE REST, FIRST?

JUST A *LITTLE* -SNARF-SNARF-

BETCHA CAN'T FLY *UNDER* THAT LOG, WILYKIT!

I SEE. IF I TAKE TIME TO GO *AROUND* IT, YOU'LL BE ABLE TO GET AHEAD!

NO WAY, WILYKAT! I CAN FLY ANYWHERE YOU CAN--

--HUH?! A *NET!* T-TURN BACK! QUICK!

I CAN'T! PANTHRO DIDN'T BUILD THESE SPACEBOARDS TO GO IN--

SPUCH

PLOK

--REVERSE!

YUCK! IT'S ALL STICKY! I CAN'T GET AWAY!

IT'S LIKE THE NET WAS PUT HERE JUST FOR *US!* LIKE SOMEONE KNEW WE COULDN'T RESIST CUTTING UNDER THAT FALLEN TREE!

WHAT'S GOING *ON*, WILYKIT?

ELSEWHERE... THIS IS THE SAME PATH WE TOOK ON OUR WAY OUT, PANTHRO, BUT I DON'T REMEMBER THESE *MUSHROOMS* BEING IN THE ROAD.

NEITHER DO I. EITHER THEY'RE AWFULLY FAST-GROWING, OR--

PUP!
PUP!
PUP!
PUP!
PUP!

--HEY! THE THUNDERTANK'S STOPPING! THAT DUST FROM THE MUSHROOMS MUST BE CHOKING THE ENGINE!

SPUTTER
SPUTT
SPUTT

THERE'S SOMETHING FUNNY ABOUT THIS!

UH-HUH. JUST AS I THOUGHT. THESE MUSHROOMS AREN'T *GROWING* AT ALL-- THEY WERE *PLACED* HERE ON PURPOSE! WHAT DO YOU THINK ABOUT THAT, TYGRA?

TYGRA?

HE'S OUT COLD! THIS DUST DOESN'T JUST WORK ON THUNDER*TANKS*...I-IT WORKS... ON TH-THUNDER...C...C...

...CAAAAAAATS...

HELP! PLEASE H-HELP ME!

SOMEONE'S IN TROUBLE!

LET'S GO!

ER, THAT IS, I'M RIGHT BEHIND YA!

THE CRIES ARE COMING FROM BEHIND THAT ROCK! I SHOULD BE THERE IN ABOUT FOUR SEC--

--WAIT! THE SAND IN FRONT OF THE ROCK! IT'S BEEN FUSED! IT'S SLICK AS GLASS!

I CAN'T GET ANY TRACTION! I CAN'T--

--STOP!

THOK

CHEETARA! A-ARE YOU OKAY?

OMIGOSH! SH-SHOULD I HELP CHEETARA, O-OR THE PERSON BEHIND THE BOULDER?

I THINK YOUR MAIN PROBLEM, LITTLE ONE--

--IS GOING TO BE HOW TO HELP YOURSELF!

TIME PASSES -- TOO MUCH TIME -- AS, BACK AT CATS' LAIR...

THEY SHOULD HAVE GOTTEN BACK BY NOW. BUT THEY'RE NOT EVEN ANSWERING THEIR CORRESPONDERS ANY MORE!

THERE'S ONLY ONE SUREFIRE WAY TO CONTACT THE THUNDERCATS, WHEREVER THEY MAY BE.

THE SWORD OF OMENS!

WITH A SURE HAND, LORD LION-O TAKES THE MYSTIC SWORD, THEN SPEAKS THE ANCIENT CHANT...

THUNDER!

THUNDER!

THUNDER!

THUNDERCATS--

--HOOOOOOOO!

THE THUNDERCAT SIGNAL SHRIEKS OUT FROM THE EYE OF THUNDERA, FILLING THE SKY BEYOND CATS' LAIR.

CLEARLY IN SIGHT AS FAR EAST AS THE CAVE OF TIME--

--AS FAR WEST AS THE RO-BERBIL VILLAGE--

--AS FAR NORTH AS THE FOREST OF THE MANTICORES--

--AND AS FAR SOUTH AS THE RIVER OF DESPAIR.

YET FOR ALL ITS VISIBILITY--

--IT DOES SURPRISINGLY LITTLE GOOD.

NOTHING! THE THUNDERCATS HAVE NEVER FAILED TO ANSWER THE SIGNAL BEFORE!

SOMETHING'S WRONG! TERRIBLY WRONG!

I'VE GOT TO FIND THE THUNDERCATS!

YES, LION-O, SEEK YOUR FRIENDS. PERHAPS YOU SHALL EVEN SUCCEED IN RESCUING THEM.

MORE LIKELY, YOU SHALL BE DESTROYED IN THE ATTEMPT!

THIS IS GOING BETTER THAN I EXPECTED!

THE SEARCH LASTS FOR HOURS, AND EVENTUALLY FAR FROM CATS' LAIR...

THE SPORE LEADS HERE. CAT-SCENT IS STRONG. BUT...IT'S NOT A SCENT I RECOGNIZE. WHO COULD--

--BY THUNDERA!

RUINS! THE REMAINS OF SOME ANCIENT THIRD EARTH CITY!

DOESN'T LOOK VERY INVITING, BUT THAT'S WHERE THE TRAIL LEADS! SO, LIKE IT OR NOT, I'D BETTER--

--EH? THE EYE OF THUNDERA! WARNING ME OF DANGER!

HRMMM

THINGS ARE NOT ALWAYS AS THEY SEEM, YOUNG LORD.

JAGA? WH-WHAT DO YOU MEAN?

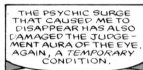

THE PSYCHIC SURGE THAT CAUSED ME TO DISAPPEAR HAS ALSO DAMAGED THE JUDGE-MENT AURA OF THE EYE, AGAIN, A TEMPORARY CONDITION.

BUT FOR NOW, YOU MUST DISREGARD ITS WARNINGS. TRUST ME-- IT IS PERFECTLY SAFE TO ENTER THE FALLEN CITY.

THE EYE HAS NEVER BEEN WRONG BEFORE, BUT... JAGA WOULDN'T LIE TO ME!

I GUESS IT MUST BE SAFE TO--

46

"LYNXANA -- I'VE HEARD THAT NAME BEFORE! BUT I WAS SO *YOUNG* --

AS WAS I. PERHAPS THAT'S WHY IT ALL HAPPENED.

CLEAR YOUR MIND, CUB, AND I'LL REFRESH YOUR MEMORY. THINK BACK...

".. TO A TIME WHEN THUNDERA WAS WHOLE.

"I WAS A NOBLE, AS WERE THE OTHER THUNDERCATS --

"-- WHEN A POSITION OF RESPONSIBILITY OPENED UP WITHIN MY TRIBE. AS THE ELDEST OFFSPRING, I LOOKED FORWARD TO THE HONOUR AND CHALLENGE OF TAKING THAT OFFICE.

"THERE WAS MUCH CELEBRATION.

"BUT WHEN THE APPOINTMENT WAS ANNOUNCED, IT WAS NOT MY NAME THAT WAS CALLED -- IT WAS MY *BROTHER'S*!

"FOR IN THOSE DAYS, TRADITION HELD THAT MALES WERE MORE DESERVING OF POWER.

"I WAS ANGRY, I FELT BETRAYED, AND I SWORE THAT WHAT *SHOULD* HAVE BEEN MINE WOULD STILL *BE* MINE --

"-- ONE WAY OR ANOTHER!"

"AND SO I LED FRIENDS AND LOYAL FOLLOWERS IN AN *ARMED REBELLION*, DETERMINED TO TAKE THE POWER I DESERVED. BUT...

"...I FAILED.

"AND THUS, WAS BROUGHT BEFORE *CLAUD-US* HIMSELF, YOUR *FATHER*-- AND THE LEADER OF ALL THUNDERA.

"HIS JUDGEMENT WAS MERCIFUL AND, AT LEAST TO HIS VIEWPOINT, JUST.

"I WAS *BANISHED* FROM THUNDERA, FORBIDDEN EVER TO RETURN...

"....EVER TO SEE MY HOME AGAIN.

"I SPENT THE YEARS THAT FOLLOWED WANDERING THE GALAXY, POLISHING MY FIGHTING SKILLS.

"I HAD TO, JUST TO *SURVIVE*!

"I EVEN FOUND A WAY TO MAKE A LIVING WITH THOSE SKILLS--

"--BY BECOMING THE MOST SUCCESSFUL AND DREADED *BOUNTY HUNTER* IN *SPACE*!

N FACT, THAT'S WHY I'M HERE. I LEARNED THAT
ANET PLUN-DARR HAD OFFERED A BOUNTY FOR
E THUNDERCATS!

WANTED
LARGE REWARD

"THE AMOUNT WAS QUITE GENEROUS, BUT NO ONE HAD HAD THE COURAGE--OR MOTIVATION TO COLLECT IT..."

...UNTIL *NOW!* YOUR FRIENDS HAVE ALREADY BEEN TRAPPED AND TURNED OVER TO THE MUTANTS OF CASTLE PLUN-DARR, CUB.

AND *YOU* WILL BE THE ICING ON THE CAKE!

IT HAS INDEED BEEN LONG SINCE YOU'VE DEALT WITH THUNDERCATS, LYNXANA!

OTHERWISE YOU'D NOT MAKE THE MISTAKE OF *UNDERESTIMATING* US!

HOOOOOOO!

WHA--THE SWORD! I--IT'S DISRUPTING THE FORCE FIELD!

51

SOMETHING'S NOT RIGHT!

SWORD OF OMENS--

--GIVE ME SIGHT BEYOND SIGHT!

YOU ARE WISE, FELINE--AND *LUCKY!*

IT SEEMS THERE NO MORE NEED FO THIS CHARADE, GOOD...

...FOR I AM MUCH MOR COMFORTABLE IN MY TRU FORM! THAT OF--

--MUMM-RA, THE EVER-LIVING!

THAT...THAT CREATURE! I-I ALL MY TRAVELS I'VE NEVE SEEN ANYTHING SO...SO EVIL

52

I ORIGINALLY CAPTURED JAGA'S SPIRIT AND TOOK HIS PLACE IN ORDER TO MISADVISE YOU, TO ERODE THE THUNDERCATS' STRENGTH FROM WITHIN!

THE EFFORTS OF THIS *RENEGADE* CAT IN AIDING MY MUTANT ALLIES WAS UNEXPECTED, BUT MOST WELCOME.

FOR NOW THERE WILL BE NO ONE TO ANSWER YOUR CRIES FOR HELP--

--WHEN I *DESTROY* YOU!

GHAAAA!

HIS MUMM-RA SEEKS OF CRUELTY, OF WICKEDNESS, AND PAIN! I'VE NEVER ENCOUNTERED A BEING SO VILE!

IF THE MUTANTS I SERVE ANSWER TO *THIS* THING, I MAY HAVE MADE A TERRIBLE MISTAKE!

NO ONE DESERVES TO FALL TO A MONSTER LIKE THAT! NO ONE!

NOT EVEN--

--A THUNDERCAT!

?!

LYNXANA!

SHHRAK

THANKS! BUT YOUR STUN-BOLTS WON'T DO ANY GOOD!

MUMM-RA IS IMMORTAL! OUR WEAPONS HAVE NO EFFECT ON HIM!

NO? THEN MAYBE--

--HIS OWN WEAPONS WILL!

I GET IT! SHE'S DISTRACTED MUMM-RA! HE'S NOT CONCENTRATING SO HARD ON FOCUSING HIS POWER BLASTS!

AND THAT SHOULD ALLOW ME TO USE THE SWORD OF OMENS--

CH-POOM

--TO SEND THOSE BLASTS BACK TO HIM!

EYYAAAAAAA!

IT'S WORKING! HIS OWN POWER IS TURNING HIM BACK INTO HIS DECAYING MUMMY FORM!

54

I OWE YOU A LOT, LYNXANA. I'D HAVE BEEN IN BIG TROUBLE IF YOU HADN'T PITCHED IN.

BUT JAGA IS STILL IN MUMM-RA'S POWER! AND WITH THE OTHER THUNDERCATS HELD CAPTIVE--

-- I NEED YOUR HELP NOW MORE THAN EVER!

I OFFER YOU TRUCE, LYNXANA, AND MY HAND. WILL YOU TAKE THEM?

UNDER THE CIRCUMSTANCES, AND CONSIDERING MY PART IN ALL THIS, I GUESS I CAN FORGET MY ANGER A BIT.

YOU'VE GOT YOURSELF A NEW PARTNER, CUB!

FOR NOW...

WAY BACK...WHEN?
PART TWO

Plot **SIMON FURMAN** ● Story **STEVE ALAN** ● Illustrations **RADBOURNE** and **BASKERVILLE** ● Colour **STEVE WHITE**

Beyond an onyx pyramid, where the marble domes and jade towers of a magnificent palace climbed high into the cloudless sky, two proud veterans of a mighty warrior race squared off in the final stages of an epic clash. Raby and Crudge, Imperial Thugron Duty Guards to the Palace of Pharoah Ka-Rey-Bar, were having a cursing contest.

'You mouldering, ring-tailed draggleworm,' snarled Raby, savouring every poisonous syll-able. 'I'll hit you so hard it'll stun your entire midden-foraging family!' 'Why you square lipped, bilge-sucking tree locust,' gasped the outraged Crudge. 'May the plague of a thousand hives be visited on your pestilent carcass!' Crudge folded his arms with the triumphant glee of one who knows the day is his. '*Snarf.*' Crudge wheeled, his rich green complexion draining to the colour of withered leaves. '*What* did you call me?' he roared, seizing Raby by the lapels of his battle tunic.

'Answer me, you ill-uttering sack of dungeon sweepings, or I'll...'

'*Snarf, snarf...*' This time there was no doubt from which direction the voice had come, as Raby and Crudge glanced down at a scratty, yellow bearded cat creature. 'Top o' the mornin' to ya, gents,' grinned Snarf. 'Any idea where the Thundercats might be hangin' out?'

The two Thugron guards exchanged arch looks, swaggering heavily around the nervously blinking Thundercat. Clouds of fine sand rose, as Snarf sneezed explosively, 'Well, well, well,' said Raby. 'Look what the Living Ooze washed up,' completed Crudge. Both Thugrons erupted in a hurricane of ugly laughter.

'Think ah'm funny, do ya?' Snarf's expression became sulky. 'Then taste the vengeance of Snarf the Fierce!' There was an anguished howl as Snarf launched a sharp kick at the booted foot of Crudge, who hopped into the path of his fellow guard. Both Thugrons clambered ungraciously to their feet in thundrous pursuit, reeling off a list of imaginative torments to which the fleeing Snarf would be subjected when caught. However, as they rounded the palace wall, their stampede was cut short.

A mountain was in the way. A mountain of furiously quivering blue flesh which turned the sky black, their knees to water, and cast a shadow across the distant landscape. Somewhere near the summit a small pair of ridiculous (and quite useless) red wings fluttered foolishly. 'You're all going to die a most grisly death!' bellowed the Astral Moat Monster. Then Raby did something which, during several months in the barrack convalescent hall, he would come to regard as the least sensible move of his career. He giggled. And was immediately swatted some fifty metres across the palace grounds. He did not get up. 'Now,' said Snarf, as the whimpering Crudge sank to his knees. 'Any idea where the Thundercats might be hangin' out?'

'Welcome to my humble abode, Thundercats!' Mumm-Ra stood on a central dais in the opulent, bejewelled throne room of Pharoah Ka-Rey-Bar. Before him, each of the securely manacled Thundercats was roughly prodded, at spearpoint, to kneel before the great onyx throne. 'Get your laughs while you can, mean green,' said Panthro. 'Before the Big Cheese gets back and catches you makin' free with the Family seat'.

There was a sharp temperature drop in the throne room as cruel winds gusted across the kneeling Thundercats, converging in a whirlpool around the cackling Mumm-Ra. When his cloak swirled open, there stood the tall and imposing figure of another man, resplendent in the Imperial golden body armour of a Pharoah. The dark, strong-boned face radiated

wisdom and compassion, but when he spoke the voice was unchanged; evil, taunting, clotted with malice. 'I don't think so, vermin,' laughed Mumm-Ra. 'You see, I *am* Pharoah Ka-Rey-Bar!'

Lion-O raised his head, expression taut and grim as he spoke. 'I'm puzzled, Mumm-Ra. If you're the true power on First Earth, why create a Pharoah at all? Why not rule yourself?' 'Ah,' said Mumm-Ra, almost fondly. 'Ever the curious feline. Very well – why shouldn't I tell you? Triumph is to be savoured.'

'I sure hope he's a slow savourer,' whispered Wilykit. Edging closer to Wilykat, she placed herself within arm's length of his manacles. Something silver flashed in her paw.

'...And order is to be maintained,' Mumm-Ra was saying. 'It seems many of my loyal subjects still have a deep distrust of sorcery, despite –' he gave a low chuckle – 'my efforts to enlighten them. And whilst Mumm-Ra alone might rule through terror, the people *love* wise Ka-Rey-Bar.' Lion-O nodded imperceptibly to Cheetara.

'You're lying, Mumm-Ra!' she chimed in. 'You have to be. If, as you said, we're a thousand years in your past, how can you possibly know about the Thundercats? We won't even be *born* for generations!'

The winds rose again, howling, as a deathly frost seemed to descend on the throne room.

'There is *nothing* I do not know of the future, or of the past!' roared the devil priest.

'I am my own beginning and my own ending! I am eternal! *I – am – Mumm-Ra, the Ever Living!*'

'So why bring us *back* in time?' joined Panthro. 'Your Third Earth incarnation not cuttin' it?'

'And what about Fourth Earth ... Fifth Earth?' heckled Tygra. 'What about the future? Does mighty Mumm-Ra *never* regain his mastery of the planet?'

Lion-O stole a sidelong glance at Wilykat and Wilykit. Unseen by either Mumm-Ra or the retinue of Thugrons, Wilykit was now picking frantically at her companion's manacles, a tiny sliver of metal darting in and out of the keyhole. The operation was taking some time, and despite their concerted efforts, Tygra's last remark had seemingly stung Mumm-Ra. Lion-O gazed yearningly at the discarded Sword Of Omens, propped by the throne of Ka-Rey-Bar.

'You'll rue the day you ever pit your puny wits against the might of Mumm-Ra!' Roared the sorceror. He was clearly running out of patience.

'You will suffer as none has suffered before when I unleash...' Lion-O heard the chink of falling tumblers as Wilykat's manacles sprang open, and leapt abruptly to his feet.

'Aw dry up, Mumm-Ra.'

'Wh-Whaaat?' Mumm-Ra's mouth hung slackly open.

'I've had it with this "might of Mumm-Ra" drivel,' jeered Lion-O. If you're going to get rid of us, get *on* with it. Unless you're planning to *bore* us into submission, that is.'

'*You dare to mock Mumm-Ra*?!' The sorceror's eyes flashed a bloody, turbulent crimson as the spectral winds reached a shrieking crescendo. He seemed almost to expand in size as the room was plunged into eerie darkness. Something was forming in the air above their heads. Luminous daggers of electricity strobed across the marble walls, throwing off balls of fire that hung in the air like live coals. Then they converged on Lion-O.

Lion-O squalled in terrible anguish. It was as if some giant hand had seized him; a hand speckled with living, writhing thorns. Arms pinioned to his sides he thrashed helplessly, a swirling lightshow in the darkened throne room as the horrified Thundercats, the dumbstruck Thugrons and the cackling Mumm-Ra looked on.

Wilykat, however, was not among the audience. Weaving silently amongst their captors, he had almost reached the discarded Sword Of Omens before Mumm-Ra whirled, pinioning him with a baleful glare. 'So,' purred the devil priest, preparing to divert his sorcerous wrath elsewhere. 'Now you seek to *deceive* Mumm-Ra!' His concentration broken, the spectral vise winked out of existence, depositing the agonised Lion-O in a pitifully shrunken heap on the flagstones.

'Heck no,' said Wilykat. 'I wasn't gonna deceive you, Mumm-Ra. I was just gonna drop you where you stand.' Mumm-Ra cursed savagely, a sweep of his arm catapulting Wilykat into the arms of his fellow Thundercats, semi-conscious. 'Attacat, Kiddo,' said Panthro gravely.

Back on the central dais, Mumm-Ra had seized the Sword Of Omens, whirling it about his head in a halo of crawling light. 'Since before your race was born I have awaited the cosmic fires raging within the Eye Of Thundera, cublings,' he raged. 'How fitting that it should now become the instrument of your destruction!' He swung the sword in a broad arc, aiming it at the crouching Thundercats. 'Feel now the full, unfettered fury of Mumm-Ra, the Ever Living!'

However, Mumm-Ra's fury was destined to remain fettered a while longer. Pandemonium had erupted outside the throne room, the shriek of discharging vibro-cannons and the brutish cries of Thugrons sprawling down the corridor in pitched battle. The priceless, be-jewelled doors of the throne room of Ka-Rey-Bar bowed suddenly inwards, groaning, and seconds later both doors and a generous portion of the castle wall caved in as a tidal wave of thundering blue flesh cascaded into the room. The Astral Moat Monster shook his head, dazed Thugrons spilling from his monstrous flanks like so many straw dolls.

One rider remained aboard, however, and the last of Mumm-Ra's dank shadow-spells lifted from the throne room as the six Thundercats called his name, laughing. 'Snarf!'

'None other. Sorry about the delay, guys — looks like I caught the later time warp! And don't worry, Scumm-Ra, y' can gimme the keys to the city later, snarf snarf...'

Before Snarf's sentence was over Lion-O had launched himself into the air, wrestling the distracted Mumm-Ra to the stone floor. The sorceror scrabbled frantically for purchase on the Sword Of Omens, but the mystic blade seemed almost to squirm, eel-slick from his fingers as it sailed into the waiting grasp of its one true owner; the Lord of the Thundercats. Mixed emotions warred for a moment on Lion-O's face as he stood over the fallen Mumm-Ra, the rekindling surge from the Sword Of Omens coursing through him as he raised the blade high above his head...

...And swung around, slicing effortlessly through the wrought-iron manacles of his fellow Thundercats. As the Astral Moat Monster dispatched the last of the Thugron guards with little apparent effort, each of the Thundercats joined Lion-O on the throne-room dais, forming a circle about the cowering Mumm-Ra. No-one was smiling.

'Let's have ourselves a little re-cap, fungus face,' said Panthro, breathing heavily. 'Especially that part about the "unfettered fury of Mumm-Ra the Ever Living".'

'Sp-Spirits of Ancient Evil,' stammered Mumm-Ra,' gesturing hysterically. 'SAVE MEEEE!'

With a sound like the tolling of some celestial bell, harsh cracks rippled up the walls of the throne room, forming a jagged necklace about the vaulted ceiling. Then the roof was torn off. All watched, transfixed, as the mighty, domed lid of the palace of Ka-Rey-Bar lifted off into the lightning-flecked heavens, roaring like a great starship.

'Bills'll be enormous', said Tygra absently. Moments later all the Thundercats were snatched aloft on the invisible fingers of the storm, the ranting Mumm-Ra, the devasted palace and a vaguely forlorn Astral Moat Monster dwindling in a giddying spiral beneath them. Lion-O's last sight before blacking out was of the palace courtyard, where a band of assorted humanoid and alien creatures stormed the gates, their triumphal cheers audible even above the buffeting winds. At the head of the group was a familiar, anthropoid figure. They wore no chains. 'Way to go,

Zar-Thule!' cried Lion-O; but his voice was lost in the baying of the cyclone.

They awoke in a cornfield on the edge of a dense forest, the sky now cloudless, a warm breeze of pollen wafting on the afternoon air. 'Hooo, boy,' grimaced Wilykit, shaking to clear her buzzing senses. 'I just made planetfall without a spaceship.'

'You are safe now, my Thundercats,' said a rich, soothingly familiar voice. The warm air shimmered for a moment, the pale, astral form of Jaga the Wise rising from the ground ahead of the Thundercats. 'Like smoke of dandelion breaking along the winds of time, you have come home.'

'Come again?' squinted Snarf.

'To the Plain of Fertility — to *Third* Earth.'

'We're all grateful, Jaga,' said Cheetara, climbing unsteadily to her feet. 'But with all of time to choose from, what's to stop Mumm-Ra trying again?' Jaga smiled patiently, his ghostly face a mesh of wrinkles. 'Mumm-Ra will have to explore other avenues of mischief now, my Thundercats. I will see that the dimensional portal remains sealed.'

'Hey,' piped Snarf, scanning the assembly. 'Where's ol' Moatie? I was gettin' along pretty good with the big lunk.'

'Indeed,' said Jaga. 'Each of us owes the Astral Moat Monster a great debt of gratitude. However, I suspect he will find happiness, even on First Earth.' Then they rose together and went out into the afternoon, heading across the Plain of Fertility to the Cat's Lair.

In two gruelling days of cheerless trudging, the Astral Moat Monster had encountered only one settlement. The villagers fled in a screaming tide as he passed. When the Moat Monster cast a doleful eye over the town from a hilltop that evening, they were already burning him in effigy. It would be easy to take offence. In fact the Moat Monster was beginning to take an extremely dim view of the universe when he eventually burst into a sun-dappled clearing.

It couldn't be. But it was. Wide, deep, its magical waters sparkling in a kaleidoscope of colour — the Astral Moat. Of course! In the dim, thousand year past of First Earth the Moat was still quite intact, undiminished by the march of time. The cooling waters sang gently as the Astral Moat Monster waded in, face spraining severely in his first smile for a millennium.

A sudden thrashing noise in the undergrowth, the sound of an enraged colossus, cut short the Moat Monster's planned evening of mindless contentment. An unpleasant thought struck him. If he was indeed a thousand years in his own past, surely the original Astral Moat Monster — his younger self — existed also? As if to confirm this theory the nearby trees were savagely uprooted, a mountainous blue apparition swaying into view. The two Astral Moat Monsters surveyed each other in mutual ugliness for a moment, steam chuffing from their nostrils.

'Great wings,' said the newcomer at last.

'Yes,' said the Astral Moat Monster. 'Yes, I sort of like them.'

THE END 🐾